A Garden for

GRACE

Ellen Mainville

Designed and published by ABCarlson Publishing, Keene NH.
ISBN: 978-0-9962883-2-3
Library of Congress Control Number: 2021943769

Photographs: Author's, courtesy Mark Mainville; Ellen's gardens, courtesy Mark Mainville and Ann Carlson; Grace Patten, from author's family album — all used with permission.

Bible quotation: New King James Version (Thomas Nelson Publishers, 1975).

Cover design: Ann Carlson and Andrew Mainville, from a photograph by Ann Carlson

Poem "Zinnia" (p. 41): previously published; *Foothills Art Society*, Malone, NY. (Issue 2, June 2008).

For

The flower gardeners

My grandmother
Grace Dupee Patten
and my mother
Louise Berry Patten

And the men who taught me
to love farm, woods and gardens

My grandfather
Howard Patten
and my dad
Robert Patten

And

Special thanks to
Foothills Art Society
for assistance with
the posthumous publication
of this volume

"Daffodowndilly has now come to town
in a petticoat green and a bright yellow gown"
(Old English Nursery Rhyme)

A Garden for Grace

A Garden for Grace
Baby's Breath on her face
Queen Anne makes her lace

Fox Glove for her hand
Lady Slippers to stand
Marigold wedding band

Jacob's Ladder to climb
Four 'o Clocks to tell time
Bells of Ireland to chime

A Forget-Me-Not place
A Dandelion space
A Garden for Grace

Crocus

Under a snow comforter
nestled in dried grass
a purple bud of crocus
sits up quick to ask

For a tiny glass of water
little bit of light
it seems like time to wake up
from the winter's night

Trillium

Spring has come with a breath still cold
and snow white trilliums unfold
My coat unzipped, my hat is shed
I let the sunshine warm my head

Turning my face to feel the sun
I think of summer just begun
with trilliums instead of snow
and soon the hay and grass to mow

Tulip

Red tulips dressed in coats today
with white snow collars
though it's May

How strange that they should be dressed so
when yesterday
I had to mow

Violets

My grandma took me as a child
to search for violets growing wild
we wandered through her memories
and gathered violets under trees

And as we sat down in the grass
to watch the mayflies dip and pass
with quiet voice her stories knit
a blanket — curled me up in it

I laid my head down on her knees
lulled to sleep by droning bees
and dreamed her young and gay and fair
with violets in her auburn hair

Mother's Day Flowers

A hanging bunch of flowers came
filled with your love
and holding your name

I held the flowers, white and red
and wished I were holding
you instead

Mayflower
(Spring Beauty)

I have gone a sailing
over the oceans blue
I plan to sail around the world
to see a thing or two

My sails are cotton sheets
pinned to an old clothesline
my boat is made of little logs
of sweetly scented pine

But my ocean is the best
that ever it could be
billows of blue mayflowers
under the maple tree

Columbine

See the starlings!
Oh my, starlings!
See the starlings
with
columbine!

Birds and flowers
play together
beaks and blossoms
intertwine

Lily of the Valley

Bending over needlework
in dimly shaded light
petticoats of deep green silk
and caps of linen white

Lilacs

In my hands a photo
of my Mom when she was young
holding purple lilacs
in early morning sun

Smiling for the camera
on the front porch of her home
no thoughts yet of children
with lilacs of their own

Bachelor Buttons

Kittens sitting in bright windowsills
playing in pots of feathery frills
batting, biting and eating a few
white and burgundy, pale pink and blue

Bachelor buttons, twisty and bent
velvety mittens, tired and spent
kittens curled into tight balls of purr
halo of blossoms twined in their fur

Iris

In the first breath of morning air
I combed the tangles from my hair
and little knots of whimsy flew
to rest upon the morning dew
and to my sleepy mind it seemed
the iris caught my midnight dream

The iris caught my midnight dream
and wore it like a shawl of cream
around a gown of purple silk
then like a nightgown, white as milk
bright dreams of summer kissed her hair
in the first breath of morning air

Peony

Here's my Grandma's peony vase
on table cloth of handmade lace
embracing mounds of fragrant blooms
the breath of springtime through my rooms

Fond memories come back to me
a garden near a maple tree
Grandma's peonies, bright-faced there
always enough for her to share

If I could slip back to the day
before she put her vase away
when peony clouds, white and pink
fresh cut, filled up her kitchen sink

I'd hug her tight and kiss her face
arrange her flowers in our vase
pretend the peonies this May
she gathered for me yesterday

Buttercup

In the field a Jersey cow
gentleness upon her brow
deep brown eyes with lashes long
hay is sweet, the sun is strong

'Round her feet the buttercup
lifting tiny petals up
smiles at her with sun's own face
and for God's bounty, says a grace

Daisy

When picking daisies from the sides
of paths where baby often rides
I put them in his stroller seat
to gently tickle his bare feet
it makes him smile and I don't care
if baby put them in his hair
and if because he's missing lunch
he snacks upon a tasty bunch
I won't be one to steal his joy
I kiss his cheeks, my baby boy

27

Marigold

Mari-gold
and
Kari-gold
and
Sari-gold
have come

Golden-headed sisters
playing in the sun
whispering their secrets
to the morning breeze
bending to its wishes
then doing
as they please

Hollyhock

A hollyhock blossom
turned upside down
becomes a fair maiden
in a ball gown

With skirts of pink satin
or purple or blue
but nothing to find
when you look for her shoe

29

Pansy

Pansies are for sisters
who live just down the street
one is yellow sunshine
with slippers on her feet

One wears a blue bonnet
tied up by bumble bees
and holds a china teapot
to brew her many teas

Happy as two sky-larks
and giddy to the core
teaching bright-eyed pansies
to wink beside their door

Welcoming all neighbors
soft velvet-coated flirts
just like pansy sisters
who dress in rainbow skirts

African Violet

On a sill above the sink
are African violets in pink
and some are purple, some are white
with leaves as velvet as the night

Grandma smiles in the early morn
bathing her grandson, the first born
she makes some cookies, bakes a pie
so much to do, and time flies by

But quiet moments in between
she pauses just to stop and lean
into the flowers on the sill
their beauty is a welcome pill

To cure the tiredness of the day
and help her chase the aches away
though she can't linger here too long
each flower sings her heart a song

Red Clover

I have a little guinea pig
I feed him on red clover
and every morning when I walk
I search the meadow over

I'm looking for the tender leaf
the succulent red flower
for gastronomical delight
at piggy's lunchtime hour

Come Pig-Pig, Piggy, Piggle-Pop,
Pig-it, Pig-Pie, Pig-Gummy,
come wake up from your little sleep
to delights for your tummy

Lupine

With spires of blossoms, pink and blue
like mountains in a distant view
or steeples calling us to pray
from sunlit churches far away

Dahlia

Just as big as a dinner plate
lunch bell ringing
don't be late

Spread a blanket on the ground
pick the dahlias
sweet and round

Invite dollies out for lunch
they can be
a cheery bunch

Give them each a flower dish
kiss their cheeks
and make a wish

I wish I may, wish I might
always see with
child-like sight

Rose

Old stones in a foundation
by a river, under trees
are ruffled with wild roses
and the buzz of honey bees

The house has long since vanished
all the family gone away
and no one picks the roses
but so faithfully they stay

They've grown across the doorstep
and played tag where once was lawn
like fragrant, pinkish footprints
of the children so long gone

Petunia

It may be a farm house
old and worn
a little tired
and forlorn

But the farm wife grows
with patient care
petunias
as if to dare

Someone to think they
might be poor
when she has jewels
at her door

Zinnia

Iz eazy sayz za zinnia
to sit here in za sun
and never, never tired I grow
when ze day iz done

I ruffle up ze petticoatz
and zipper up ze gown
put on ze yellow danzin shoez
and tiptoe into town

Ferns

One, two, three, four
ferns upon the forest floor
five, six, seven, eight
fronds uplifted like a gate
nine, ten, eleven, twelve
enter all the little elves

43

Phlox

When the phlox grow tall
and the sun shines warm
take a photo
of us on the farm

Remember the day
when happiness grew
and Grandpa posed
not wearing his shoe

Weeping Willow

Sometimes gardens have to weep
sadness comes and sunshine sleeps
buds bow down to earth below
ground is dry, cold winds blow

When pain comes with scary face
gardens make a quiet place
under weeping willow tree
gentle arms encircle me

Here with sadness I can sit
if I weep a little bit
I am better by and by
sun comes back to warm the sky

Black-eyed Susan
and
Blue-eyed Grass

Black-eyed Susan and blue-eyed grass
like Alice through the looking glass
behold the things I can not see
like whispering worms and talking bee
and open up a half-closed mind
for childhood, not quite left behind
when I could see the magic too
through eyes of other-worldly blue

Day Lily

Consider the lilies
how they bloom
they neither
toil nor reap

But glory in
the blessings of
each hour
before they sleep

King Solomon
with all his gold
could never
imitate

Rich beauty of the
day lilies
beside my
garden gate

Gladiola

Gladiola
Ice-cold cola
Faded blue jeans
Snapping string beans
On the back porch
Letting sun scorch
Ten bare brown toes
Corn neat in rows
Peas on the vine
Doing just fine
Sun is so hot
Glad that I'm not
Got a big fan
On the divan
Feeling lazy
Sky is hazy
Music drifts by
Clouds are so high
Gram's Victrola
Gladiola

Sunflower

I speak Sunflower
do you?
I speak it to the
morning dew
and to the little snails
that creep
and to the tiny frogs
that sleep
"Beware!" I say,
"The sun has come
Quick, hide yourselves
you'd better run!"
I shout the warning
but my heart
rejoices in the
golden start
of heat and sun and
blazing air
I shout, "Sunflower,
have a care!"
and laugh to see
the fire begun
the burning days
of summer sun

Autumn Trees

Autumn trees are blushing
caught with petticoats down
golden tulle and taffeta
fallen in circles around

Shyly they are waiting
shivering in the night
for winter's hand to wrap them
in soft flannels of pure white

Pearly Everlasting

The geese are flying low today
the maple is in bright array
and pearly everlasting nods
beside the bursting milkweed pods
summer's gone away

Geranium

I love to pass a windowpane
when snow is drifting down
and see a breath of June remain
still somewhere in my town

Geraniums in scarlet red
Geraniums in white
Geraniums behind the glass
safe from December's night

Poinsettia

Not a flower
but a leaf
red, like Grandpa's
handkerchief

Goodnight Garden

Goodnight garden
Goodnight weeds
Goodnight summer
Hello seeds

Hello bedtime
Hello frost
Hello fireside
Goodnight moss

Goodnight flowers
Goodnight bees
Goodnight hammock
Hello skis

Killer Frost

R.I.P.

Seeds To Hatch

My Grandmother

My grandmother, Grace Dupee Patten, was a farm wife. The work of the farm didn't give her much time to spend on her flowers. And yet, she had flowers: violets, iris, daffodils, phlox, peonies, wild roses, a lilac bush as big as a small house, trilliums dug up from the family wood-lot, mayflowers like a carpet of blue under the clothesline. Flowers surrounded the house and, I think, lived in her heart as well as in her garden. I remember weeding the garden with her as she taught me the flowers, like reciting the names of close neighbors and old friends. "This iris has one of the sweetest scents…like springtime with fresh, misty rain. And this wild rose, it's been here longer than I have…longer than my mother and father…it came with the very first settlers ever to turn up the soil. And this peony, deep crimson…an uncommon color…I worry about it being crowded out…I think I should transplant it, but peonies don't take well to change. These golden glows, always plant them in the back…a beautiful halo of gold over the garden, but if you put them in the front, they hide everything…"

I learned, she taught…and when I moved away, I took a little bit of everything with me. I carried away my grandmother's garden.

A garden will always be a part of my life; each flower evokes a different memory. Some bring me into the farmhouse kitchen, some take me back through the cow pasture and onto the banks of the Deer River, some remind me of hanging clothes on the line on a hot summer day, some take me to a quiet and shady place under the windows of my childhood home…all of them make me think of my grandmother.

This book is for my grandmother, Grace Dupee Patten, and the garden of joy she planted in my heart.

"the bluebell is the
sweetest flower
that waves
in summer air"
(Emily Brontë)

60

Grandma's Gift

Grace Patten with Dale (left) and Ellen

Grandma's hand wrapped round my own
child to adult I have grown

Greeting flowers one by one
warmed and kissed by summer sun

Just like friends I know so well
iris, phlox, violet, bluebell

Friends still with me to this day
though my Grandma couldn't stay

Joy tucked in a flower's face
sweet gift from my Grandma Grace

About the Author

Ellen and Mark Mainville

Ellen Mainville (1955-2021) lived in Northern New York with her husband Mark and poodle Coco—in a Victorian house with abundant flower gardens. Many of these flowers came originally from her grandmother Grace, on the farm where Ellen was raised. They were carefully transplanted from place to place, wherever she moved: their origin, growing patterns, and method of propagation meticulously documented in her "garden diary." Ellen previously published *All My Days* (2017), an illustrated book of meditations. She was 98% finished with *A Garden For Grace* when she became a casualty of the great pandemic of 2020-21: victim of an autoimmune condition combined with vaccine-breakthrough Covid-19. Yet even at the end, as she knew her God was calling her home, Ellen was giving instructions for the completion of her book. It is the gift of her heart to all who knew or will come to know her.

Ellen gave Andrew, one of her two sons and himself an artist and poet, creative control for completing the volume. Andrew tells of "a vision I had as a child: of my mother strolling in her garden in the early morning hours. This garden she poured her love into, creating and cultivating beauty within the borders she designed at our old house in New York. I can still see the delight in her—a small smile ever present upon her face—as she admired God's gift of beauty on this earth. It's a vision that will never leave me, just as flowers will always remind me of her love."

Ellen was many things to many people: a granddaughter, daughter, wife, mother, grandmother, sister, aunt, niece, cousin and friend. Augmenting her long career as a teacher in public and private schools, she was counselor, preacher, writer, poet, artist, singer, gardener, seamstress, cook, baker, consummate hostess, and so much more. No litany of titles or roles can capture the wise, funny, compassionate, and engaging person that will be so sorely missed by all who loved her. And yet, she is here to be found in her words and her drawings. Enjoy!

Ellen's gardens

Acknowledgments

I thank God, who makes me to lie down in green pastures and leads me beside the still waters. He restores my soul, and my cup runs over with joy—especially in a garden.

I thank my husband, Mark, who is the love of my life, my support and encourager in all things; Nathaniel, who grows his own little garden of herbs and hot spices; Andrew, who speaks "Sunflower," just as I do; Danielle, who gave me flowers; Heather, who is a rare flower in the garden of life; and Elizabeth and Abby, who grew up in my garden.

I thank my grandchildren, who are teaching me more about the joy of family life: my fun-loving boys, Deegan, Evan, and James; and my cookie-baking girls, Lana, Nova, and Azra.

I thank my sister, Ann, who has propelled me on this journey and remains always my best friend; and my brother, Dale, who remembered the details of farm and family life that I forgot.

Golden Glow

"the end of a thing
is better than its beginning"
(Ecclesiastes 7:8)

So I will not end with snow
sleeping gardens, winds that blow
I'll end with hopes of seeds to grow
and leave you with a golden glow

Index of Poems and Flowers

"the 'amen' of nature is always a flower"
(Oliver Wendell Holmes, Sr.)